SHIRE NATURAL HI

C000269567

THE
BLUE TIT

JIM FLEGG

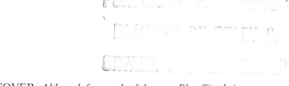

FOR REFERENCE ONLY

CONTENTS

COVER: *Although for much of the year Blue Tits thrive on a very mixed diet, when rearing their young they are heavily dependent on the seasonal abundance of a few species of moth caterpillars. Accurate timing of hatching is necessary to ensure the fast-growing brood derives benefit from the short-lived abundance of this food source.*

Series editors: Jim Flegg and Chris Humphries.

Copyright © 1987 by Jim Flegg. First published 1987.
Number 17 in the Shire Natural History series. ISBN 0 85263 716 0.
All rights reserved. No part of this publication may be reproduced or transmitted in any form or by any means, electronic or mechanical, including photocopy, recording, or any information storage and retrieval system, without permission in writing from the publishers, Shire Publications Ltd, Cromwell House, Church Street, Princes Risborough, Aylesbury, Bucks HP17 9AJ, UK.

Set in 9 point Time~ ~~~~~ ~~~ ~~~~~~ ~~ ~~~~~ ~~~~~~~ by C. I. Thomas & Sons (Haverfordwest)   Haverfordwest, Dyfed.

OTLEY COLLEGE LIBRARY

009731

Introduction

Almost everyone living in Britain or Ireland is likely to see Blue Tits, except on the remoter islands to the north and west of Scotland. Though they are ancestrally birds of broad-leaved forest, they are extremely versatile and have adapted well to twentieth-century life in man-modified habitats as diverse as conifer plantations and urban gardens, even penetrating to the hearts of cities. They are one of the main reasons that bird-watching from a house is seldom dull, because they are frequent visitors to any feeding table. They are small birds, around 4½ inches (11 cm) long, generally bright blue and green above, with a startlingly electric blue cap over a white face, and with yellow underparts, sometimes showing a greyish line down the centre of the breast.

The tit family, the Paridae, contains between sixty and seventy different species, most of which originate in the northern hemisphere. There are no tits in South America, nor in Australasia. In Europe there are eleven species, discounting the Bearded Tit *(Panurus biarmicus)*, which is now thought not to be a relative of the tits, though its relationships with other families are far from clear.

Eight of these eleven species have been recorded in Britain and Ireland: Coal Tit *(Parus ater)*, Great Tit *(Parus major)*, Blue Tit *(Parus caeruleus)*, Crested Tit *(Parus cristatus)*, Marsh Tit *(Parus palustris)*, Willow Tit *(Parus montanus)*, Long-tailed Tit *(Aegithalos caudatus)*, and Penduline Tit *(Remiz pendulinus)*. Of these, the last two fall into separate subfamilies. The Penduline Tit is an extremely scarce vagrant to Britain, and the Crested Tit, though widespread in continental Europe, is confined to a few areas predominantly of old pine forest in the Scottish Highlands. The others are more or less widely distributed year-round residents in Britain and Ireland (though much of Scotland and all of Ireland lack the Marsh and Willow Tits). None could be confused with the Blue Tit, because of its predominantly blue upper parts. The remaining three European tits are the Siberian Tit *(Parus cinctus)*, Sombre Tit *(Parus lugubris)* and Azure Tit *(Parus cyanus)*. Though predominantly an eastern Eurasian bird, the Azure Tit breeds as far west as Poland and seems to be expanding its range westward. Perhaps one day it will join the list of British and Irish tits. Rather larger than a Blue Tit, it is mainly white below, with upper parts of various shades of blue and blue-grey. Its white crown quickly distinguishes it from the Blue Tit.

Blue Tits have long been widespread, numerous and popular. Evidence for this comes from the many and various local names for the bird. These range from the obvious 'Blue Bonnet' and 'Pickcheese' to oddities like 'Nun' (because of the similarity of its head pattern to a nun's habit), 'Billy Biter' (perhaps as it pecks vigorously around twigs and buds in winter) and 'Heckymal'. This last may be a derivation from the Old English *Hicemase* for the Blue Tit, and *mase* or variants of it occur as suffixes for tits in several languages: *mees* in Dutch, *meise* in German, *mes* in Swedish and *mesange* in French. The Anglo-Saxon word *mase* was applied to any sort of small bird and is not connected with the word 'mouse', to which it was corrupted a few centuries ago in the word 'titmouse', (the plural of which should therefore be 'titmouses' and not 'titmice'). By the time of Yarrell, who published his *British Birds* in 1843, the shortened form 'tit' had established itself in common use. There is a suggestion that 'tit' is derived from the Icelandic *tittr*, again meaning a small bird or indeed anything small.

Some of the old colloquial names for the Blue Tit are derived from its shrill calls, like 'Tichife' and 'Pinchem', but most modern bird identification books offer transliterations like 'tsee-tsee-tsee-tsit' and 'tsee tsitsee-pew' for its most frequent calls. There is also a commonly used harsh scolding churr, and in spring Blue Tit males will choose high perches to produce their song, which opens with two or three call notes, followed by a monotone but musical trill: 'tsee-tsee-tsee tsu-hu-hu-hu-hu-hu-hu'.

Today the popularity of the Blue Tit stems from its attractive appearance, its abundance, its presence in so many and varied habitats, and from its approachability. Though binoculars are useful when watching Blue Tits, the birds allow such a close approach that they may be unnecessary. Blue Tits are amongst the most agile of avian feeders, perhaps the most nimble of all. They have no problems in hanging upside-down on swinging fat, peanuts or a half coconut in the garden, sometimes holding on with only one foot. Perhaps this should not be surprising, as their ancestral natural habit is to feed on the extreme ends of branches. Much of the time, away from the bird table, they are seeking out insects (and other arthropods) and their eggs and larvae when they probe around the buds and twigs. In this way they eliminate a tremendous number of insects (see later) and when they may be suspected of attacking prize buds it is usually insects or their eggs that they are searching for, tucked away in crevices in the bark. But they are not always wholly beneficial: attacks on milk bottles and ripe fruit damage are also dealt with later.

The Blue Tit is amongst the most opportunist of birds in its feeding techniques and diet and birds as a group are very catholic in their choice of diet. The ingenuity that Blue Tits apply to obtaining food from bird tables and feeders in the garden is regularly seen but students of bird behaviour have set quite complicated puzzles for tits to solve before receiving a food reward for their efforts, and the Blue Tit has an outstanding record in overcoming these problems. The 'intelligence tests' set by experimenters include pulling up food hanging at the end of a string: many Blue Tits will quickly learn to pull up a loop, grasp it between toes and perch, reach down to pull up another loop, grasp it, and so on until the food is within reach. A few will even learn to wind the string by rotating a moving perch like a winch. Other tests involve pulling out a series of pegs to release food, or removing a locking peg before pulling open a drawer. The solving of such problems should not be associated with intelligence tests as applied to humans. The activities and achievements have been cited as possible examples of 'insight learning' by W. H. Thorpe, and clearly Blue Tits are leaders in the production of such new, adaptive responses arising from what might be termed 'insight' or in solving problems by the rapid adaptation of previous experiences. Nonetheless, despite this opportunism and adaptability, there remains a typically avian tendency to stereotyped responses to new situations. C. M. Perrins quotes what happened after the Second World War: peanuts, as avidly fed upon in the 1930s as they are now, had been unavailable during the war. Once they were again available, bird lovers put out peanuts again, only to see them remain uneaten for many weeks, until a few individuals tried the 'new' food source. Once rediscovered, the habit spread quickly through the population, perhaps a benefit of spending part of the year in flocks.

Blue Tits are renowned for frequently choosing extraordinary nest sites, including bottles, tin cans, boxes, all sorts and sizes of pipes (vertical, horizontal, or sloping), letter boxes, car dashboards, glove compartments and radiators. Most years there are reports of Blue Tits nesting in post boxes, and normally the Post Office requests that the box is not used during the breeding season. More usual nest sites are holes or crevices in trees or rocky or earthy banks, including cavities in quarries, walls or other masonry, and occasionally derelict rat holes or rabbit burrows.

The Blue Tit will readily accept man-made nesting sites. Nestboxes in gardens are commonplace, and observing them can be fascinating. All sizes of nestboxes are occupied, and a pair of Blue Tits may gather more than half a cubic foot (0.01 cubic metre) of nest material in order to use a large nestbox designed for Jackdaws or Little Owls.

For the ordinary birdwatcher, it is a pleasure and a privilege to watch at close quarters the everyday life of the Blue Tit family, but for the research ornithologist the tolerance that Blue Tits show of regular inspections of their nests, and the handling, weighing and measuring of themselves, their eggs and their young, has opened unusual fields of work, and as a result the breeding biology of the Blue Tit is more thoroughly researched than that of almost any other bird. An account of the Blue Tit's year may appropriately start in spring, at the start of the nesting season.

Spring and early summer

PAIR FORMATION

As winter draws to a close — and on warm fine days even in February — signs of territorial activity become more apparent among the Blue Tits. During the winter, loosely knit flocks have roamed the countryside, feeding as they move. In many places such flocks may well never have left the woodland, whilst in other areas they may have made several circuits of the copses, hedges and gardens of the neighbourhood. As spring approaches, these flocks become smaller and less cohesive, with birds breaking away to start their breeding cycle.

It may well be that pair bonds of some description are formed during the winter, to be cemented firmly in the spring. Certainly many female Blue Tits roost during the long winter nights in what will become the nest site. For the male, the first steps are to demarcate his territorial boundaries by singing from a series of prominent perches. Early in the season, singing activity is intense and occupies many of the daylight hours, but once territorial boundaries between neighbouring birds have become firmly established and are no longer a cause for dispute, song and the vehemence with which it is produced diminish except when a strange male enters the area. It seems that the males quickly get to know the songs of adjacent birds and instantly recognise in a newcomer a potential threat to the stability of the community.

Frequently male and female will feed together, hunting the still almost bare twigs for food. Occasionally he may need to posture to deter the approach of a rival, normally by raising the bright cobalt feathers on his crown, slightly spreading his wings and fanning his tail. Seen together at this time, the two sexes are at their most distinct: though the size difference is marginal, the practised eye can detect that the male is rather larger; certainly (though there is great individual variation in colour) he is brighter, with deeper blue tints and richer yellows, and with a sparkling iridescence to the King-fisher-like feathers on his crown.

Adult males (that is those just embarking on their second, or third or more, breeding season) are a shade larger and brighter than yearlings (about to breed for the first time), especially in the wings, where the year-old bird retains the fledgling greenish covert feathers (the small feathers between the 'shoulder' of the wing and the long, strong primary and secondary (or flight) feathers. In adults, these are all deep blue. These distinctions, visible from close by with binoculars, apply equally to the females, so there is a range of plumage brightness from adult males (the brightest) through yearling males, then adult females to yearling females (the dullest), and size follows the same pattern. In birds (as in humans) there are large individuals and small in the same sex, and some individuals are more colourful, or dowdy, than others, but the above is a good general guide, especially when several birds are about, allowing quick comparisons to be made.

Often when they are together, the female will beg food from the male, fluffing her feathers, lowering her head and fluttering her outstretched wings, and this behaviour extends right through the 'courtship' period from territory formation, often even until there are young in the nest. Victorian ornithologists named it 'courtship feeding' and considered that it played a part in cementing the pair bond, perhaps in much the same way as a courting human male will bring gifts to the female of his affections.

Modern theory is far more prosaic. There is ample evidence that the most successful breeding females are those in

1. *An adult Blue Tit with its young inside the nest.*

best condition at the outset of the breeding season — they produce larger and more productive clutches of eggs. But early in spring food is at its scarcest and the weather often cool, making feeding difficult. It seems most likely that in courtship feeding the male is assisting the female to achieve a weight gain and health status that she would find difficult to obtain alone.

NEST BUILDING

The time of the start of nest building varies from southern to northern Britain, ranging from (on average) mid to late March in the south to mid April or later in the north. Sudden climatic changes — prolonged wet or cold weather on the one hand, or a warm sunny spell on the other — can produce appreciable variation from place to place and certainly from year to year.

Nest building is normally carried out entirely by the female, though the male will often accompany her on flights to collect material and will sometimes go into the nest hole with her on returning to the nest. Early in spring, the female may spend a lot of her time in the nest, pecking away the odd chip of wood or mud from around the entrance hole, and shuffling the few pieces of moss — often all that the nest contains for several days — around on the nest floor with her breast, this probably being a form of practice for when she shapes the actual nest cup.

The first foundations may be wholly moss, but more often there is a basic framework of dead grass, dry twigs or rootlets. Often in the early days the female will arrive with a beakful of twiglets held crosswise and find it difficult or impossible to enter no matter how

5

hard she pushes. With a little experience, though, she quickly masters entry, sometimes hardly seeming to pause in her flight as she dives into the hole. In most areas, loose moss is abundant and easily collected and forms the main bulk of the nest. After two or three days of building in earnest, the layer of moss will be 3 or 4 cm (1¼ to 1½ inches) deep, and the female will begin to form a crude 'cup' in the moss, often in a corner of the nest distant from the entrance, and perhaps 4 cm (1½ inches) or more in diameter. She will then start laying her eggs, usually before the process of lining the cup is properly under way.

Blue Tits almost invariably lay an egg a day — usually early in the morning — and almost invariably the female will conceal her first few eggs haphazardly in the loose nest fabric. As the clutch nears completion, she will root out the eggs and gather them together in the cup, and the cup itself will, by constant rotation of the female's body within it, have assumed a firmer shape. At this time she will also line the cup with some finer grasses, the occasional hair and (conspicuously) with feathers. These are often obtained from corpses and in rural surroundings tend to be the leftovers from shooting or fox kills — usually Wood Pigeon or Pheasant. The former are conspicuous because of their white downy bases, the latter less practical, because they lack this good insulation property. Around farms, chicken feathers feature, but a study of the nest lining of urban and suburban Blue Tit nests presents a challenge in feather identification, with even Grey Parrot and Budgerigar feathers on record. This feather lining is a useful way of identifying Blue Tit nests, for, although Marsh and Willow Tits also use feathers, the other two

2. *Even nestboxes are vulnerable to predators. Damage of this sort is caused by Great Spotted Woodpeckers and Grey Squirrels attempting to reach the young tits.*

6

numerous species (and major users of nestboxes), Great and Coal Tits, use fur, wool and horse or cattle hairs to line their nests.

EGGS AND BROODING

The Blue Tit egg is of typical egg shape, white with a variable quantity of tiny reddish or chestnut speckles, often denser at the big end, though sometimes (perhaps when the female is elderly) these are almost lacking. They are small — about 15 by 12 mm (⅝ by ½ inch) weighing around 0.5 gram (0.02 ounce). The clutch size varies considerably with the season, with the ages of the parent birds, and with the habitat. It ranges commonly from five to sixteen eggs, occasionally fewer (normally late replacement clutches), occasionally more — though the suspicion then is that more than one female has been laying in the nest. Young females tend to lay smaller clutches than birds with previous experience, and, in general, Blue Tits in broad-leaved woodland lay larger clutches than farmland birds (by one or two eggs) and these in turn normally lay one or two eggs more than garden-breeding birds. Average clutch sizes vary in deciduous woodlands from about ten up to twelve eggs. In Britain and Ireland the huge majority of Blue Tits lay only one clutch each year, though if a predator takes the first clutch a replacement will often be laid. There are occasional exceptions, especially in coniferous woodland, and on the continent, where Blue Tits are often found in conifers or mixed woodlands, two broods each year are more normal.

As her clutch nears completion, a 'brood patch' begins to develop on the breast and belly of the female. Most of the feathers covering this area originate

3. *In order to deter predators strong metal plates need to be fixed to nestboxes.*

4. *Blue Tits often choose unusual nest sites. Here, in a newspaper delivery box, an impromptu nestbox is shared with a Wren, whose young are just visible within the right-hand nest.*

5. *A clutch of Blue Tit eggs. Twelve or more eggs in a clutch are not uncommon.*

6. *Sensing the return of an adult, young Blue Tits (still almost blind and naked) reach up, beaks open, to receive food.*

in two tracts running down the sides of the breast and on to the flanks, though there is a scanty covering of down feathers all over. These down feathers are shed on the belly, and the large area of skin exposed (by a controlled movement of the skin muscles, lifting the feathers outwards) is wrinkled and almost purple, because it is richly supplied with blood vessels just below the skin. It is the warm blood of these vessels, aided by the insulating properties of the nest and the feather 'coverlet' around the bird's breast, that provides the warmth to incubate the eggs at a temperature that promotes their development. The female alone incubates, regularly changing her position on the eggs, turning them at frequent intervals (vital to ensure that all the eggs receive equal and even warm-

ing), and several times each day leaving the nest briefly to feed and drink. Incubation may start before the final egg is laid, and usually continues for fourteen days, occasionally a day or two more or fewer.

FEEDING THE YOUNG

While the female incubates, the male has little to do, singing less often but remaining within sight of the nest hole, always ready to escort the female if she leaves the nest to feed. Once the young begin to hatch, though, he quickly becomes far more actively involved. The young hatch, tiny, naked and helpless, always in need of food and often, if the weather is cool, in need of warmth. The female removes the fragments of shell each time a chick hatches, flying some distance from the nest before dropping

9

them. The full clutch may take several hours, or even as much as a day, to hatch. If the weather is warm, the female will brood the young briefly at frequent intervals, but if it is cool she will spend much of her time brooding, and the male will do most or all of the food collecting. When the young are small, the food their parents collect is small too — aphids, tiny caterpillars, spiders and the like. As they grow, so bigger food items, especially plump caterpillars, are brought to them by the parent birds, which often each make a hundred or more visits with food daily. At each visit waste — in the form of a fecal pellet enclosed in a gelatinous sac — is collected by the adults and dropped some distance from the nest.

As the young get older and their food demands increase, their emerging feathers (and the crowded conditions in the nest) keep them sufficiently warm for the female to need to brood only at night, freeing her to help even more with the collection of unending supplies of food. Most broods will remain in the nest for at least eighteen days before they are sufficiently mature and well enough grown in the wing to fledge. Often, if the weather is poor, they will delay their departure for up to two or three days.

In farmland and gardens the food available to tits varies in quantity and quality depending on a wide range of factors: this is probably why clutch sizes in these habitats are smaller than in deciduous woodland. Here, the success of the young tits (and the stability of the tit population) is dependent on the numbers of Winter Moth *(Operophtera brumata)* and *Tortrix* moth caterpillars feeding mainly on the oaks, and on the timing of the caterpillar hatch.

In some years caterpillar numbers are so vast that on a still day their droppings, or frass, can be heard falling on the woodland floor like light rain and even huge oaks may have their leaves eaten to ribbons and be almost defoliated. But the caterpillars must complete this stage of their life cycle and descend on gossamer threads to the ground to pupate before the oak leaves become dark green, indicating the presence of tannins that make the leaves uneatable for the caterpillars. Thus, though food is abundant, it comes in a marked peak lasting only a few weeks. Usually both the timing of egg laying and the sizes of the clutches laid by Blue Tits are closely correlated to the timing and size of the caterpillar 'crop'. How the tits know what to expect, and when, remains to be discovered. It may be that common factors such as winter temperature, spring daylength, spring temperatures (and perhaps other things too) govern both tits and Winter Moths, but the value of the close association is illustrated dramatically when the system fails for some reason.

This is an irregular event, but when it happens it is easily detected by the alert birdwatcher. Well fed tit families are usually almost silent within their nests, but when very hungry they will pipe shrilly for food. If such cries are heard during a woodland walk in May or early June, then an investigation of likely nest sites (or of nearby nestboxes) will reveal a few families cold and dead, simply from starvation. Predators will hear, better than humans, the cries of the hungry young tits, and the two major predators (in many areas) of nestling tits, the Weasel and the Great Spotted Woodpecker, may wreak havoc in such seasons.

LOSSES OF EGGS AND YOUNG

Though the average clutch size of Blue Tits seems high compared with the four to six eggs of many small and medium-sized birds, these usually produce two or even three broods of young during the season. The flourishing Blue Tit population indicates that their single large brood strategy is as effective as that where multiple broods spread both the demands on the food supply and the various risks (like bad weather), across a longer season.

The evident success of Blue Tit populations contrasts with the heavy losses of eggs and young during the breeding season. Egg losses in a study of a woodland in Kent averaged about one-third of the eggs laid: sometimes just one egg in a clutch, but more often whole clutches. Amongst the egg predators able to defeat the apparent security of a nest hole are field mice, which climb in, Great Spotted Woodpeckers and Grey

Squirrels, which hack or bite their way in — particularly to nestboxes, which they may learn to recognise as likely to contain food, and Tree Sparrows. These birds may take over a Blue Tit nest hole, despite the vigorous defence that the tits will put up, and build their own nest on top of the eggs or young it contains.

Once the young have hatched, they are vulnerable, even in years of plentiful food, to the predators already mentioned, though the toll taken is not as great. On average, in the study woodland in Kent, about 15 per cent of the young hatched were lost each year in this way, and losses attributable to 'natural causes' were few. The Great Spotted Woodpecker has an ingenious technique of seizing young tits, which, as they grow older, when eager to be fed, jump up towards the entrance hole as the shadow of a returning parent bird falls across it. This the Woodpecker exploits, landing silently near the hole and reaching in to grab the hapless youngster that jumps up expectantly — the other young being out of reach as the Woodpecker can get only its head in the hole.

Thus, by mid June in the south and early July further north, most Blue Tits should have their families on the wing.

Late summer, autumn and winter

When they leave the nest, the wings of the Blue Tit juveniles are still not fully grown; the crowded conditions of the nest hole have allowed little wing exercise and almost no flight practice, so for several days their flights are short, feeble and clumsy and they do not stray far from the territory. The family keeps together, and for perhaps a couple of weeks, sometimes longer, the young depend heavily on their parents for food. As they get older and more capable, they begin to wander more, often well out of the territory in which they were raised. The late summer woodland is relatively quiet — there is much less bird song, and what there is has a leisurely quality implying that for the adults the peak of effort has passed.

MOULT

Though the woodland is quiet, everywhere birds are moving, feeding under cover. At this time the young Blue Tits can be readily distinguished from the older birds: where the adult is white, the juvenile is pale greyish yellow; the yellow on the juvenile belly has a grey-green cast to it, and where (on the crown, back, wings and tail) the adult is strikingly blue, the juvenile is a drab grey-blue, with greenish overtones. Over the next few weeks this dull plumage will be replaced (save for the flight feathers in the wing and sometimes also the tail) in the process called moult.

Feathers are essential for flight and warmth and serve many other functions, such as in display when attracting a mate. Made largely of the protein keratin, feathers inevitably wear out: some female Blue Tits have wings as much as 5 mm (0.2 inch) shorter than the normal 60-63 mm (2.4 to 2.5 inches) at the end of the breeding season. Frequent visits to the nest, wriggling each time through the narrow entrance, make feather wear particularly marked in the Blue Tit but any small bird needs to replace its feathers each year.

In contrast to many other small birds (but like the Great Tit) Blue Tits start moulting when, or sometimes even shortly before, the young leave the nest — generally early in June in the south. Moult proceeds at a leisurely pace into the autumn, and rarely is more than one primary flight feather missing from each wing (moult is symmetrical), although others will be in various stages of growth. Normally the missing flight-feather area will not exceed 20 per cent of the total, so the bird is unlikely to be much inconvenienced, although the chances, for example, of being caught by a Sparrowhawk are slightly greater.

7. *Relatively short, broad and rounded wings confer flight manoeuvrability rather than speed on the Blue Tit. This has clear practical benefits for birds that spend much of their time flitting between close-packed twigs, often moving in the wind.*

8. *Blue Tits are amongst the most regular attenders and avid feeders at bird tables during the winter months. Summer feeding is considered undesirable.*

9. *Feather care is vital for birds. Here a juvenile Blue Tit, recognisable by its drab plumage as being only a few weeks out of the nest, bathes itself.*

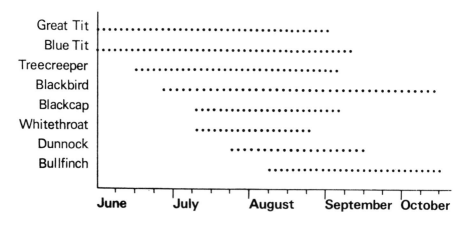

	June	July	August	September	October
Great Tit					
Blue Tit					
Treecreeper					
Blackbird					
Blackcap					
Whitethroat					
Dunnock					
Bullfinch					

10. *The moulting seasons of various small woodland birds. Blue and Great Tits are distinctive for the early start to the process of moult and for the long duration of feather replacement.*

Soon after the old ones are shed, the new feathers are secreted by special cells in the skin, and this process uses both energy and raw materials. Moult also reduces the thermal insulation of the body, again increasing the need to feed in order to keep warm. The relatively slow moult of the Blue Tit is typical of birds resident year-round, and as it occupies in the Blue Tit almost one-third of the year, 100 days, the increased energy levels and food demands that moult creates are likely to cause few problems. There are exceptions to this general rule — for example the Dunnock — which may reflect food requirements that are as yet not understood, or may even be a throwback to times past when such birds regularly migrated. For migrants (Blackcap, Whitethroat) things are very different. Having raised one or two broods, they must move away south before food supplies begin to fail and the climate to change for the worse, hence their relatively speedy moult in about 45 days compared with the Blue Tit's 100. At the height of the moult Whitethroats may have six of the ten primary feathers in each wing missing and are only just capable of flight.

Young birds face different problems: there is no need for them to change the wing feathers they have grown in the nest, for they have not had the chance to wear out. At fledging, and in the weeks that follow, they need to be as inconspicuous as possible to protect themselves (by camouflage) from predators taking advantage of their inexperience. Neither, at this time, do they want the bright plumage that might stimulate aggressive responses from adults of their kind, including even their own father. However, long before next spring they will need to be able to compete with their elders for territory and for mates. Hence in summer and early autumn the Blue Tit young moult their body feathers (and occasionally their tails) and assume the full plumage, in all its bright colours, for display purposes. This moult, too, takes many weeks, and most juveniles at this time have a ragged, parti-coloured plumage.

Detailed information on the pattern and progress of moult comes from intensive studies of ringed birds in a number of localities. Blue Tits are relatively easily caught (in traps or in nets, but only by licensed, qualified bird ringers) and even in the breeding season, with due care, the females can be lifted off their eggs and examined, and then carefully replaced. Once they feel the warmth of their eggs against the brood patch, the incubating birds quickly settle firmly back into the nest cup. The habit that Blue Tits (and others of their family) have of readily using nestboxes greatly adds to the opportunities they offer for study. Regular retrapping of individual ringed birds allows the progress of moult to be checked at intervals of a few days. On a longer time scale, movements of individuals around their habitat can be traced, a good idea of their survival rate obtained (and the time when mortality is at its highest) and changes in their weights can be recorded.

WEIGHT CHANGES

For the Blue Tit, the annual pattern of weight change is fascinating. For both male and female there is an indication of weight increase once the young have fledged in June, rising to a peak in July or August, probably coincident with the major energy demands of the middle of the moult. In late autumn average weights for both sexes fall, only to rise again to another low peak in midwinter. This coincides with the lowest temperatures and the shortest daylengths of the year, and the weight increase is thought to be made up in part of fats and other body materials stored as a short-term reserve to insure against the extra energy losses caused as birds maintain their body temperatures during the long and cold winter nights, and against the hazards of severe weather reducing still further the short daylight hours available for feeding. The other component (probably interrelated) is a layer of subcutaneous fat laid down primarily for insulation, as on a much grander scale are the blubber layers of penguins, seals and whales. This accumulation of weight begins earlier than

11. *Weight changes through the year. Note the abrupt and large rise in female weight (circles) at the start of the nesting season. L, laying begins; C, clutch laying completed; H, start of hatching; Y, growing young in nest; F, approximate time of fledging, when the young depart from the nest. Male weight is indicated by crosses.*

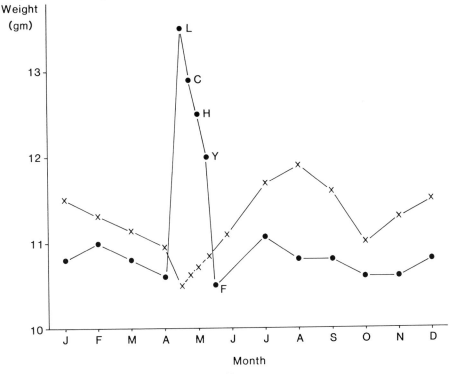

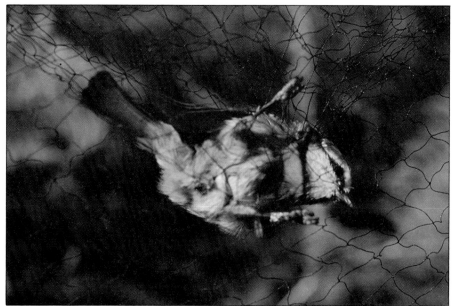

12. *A Blue Tit caught in a mist net.*

13. *Extracting a Blue Tit from a mist net. Intensive training is necessary, coupled with a gentle touch, to use this sophisticated technique to catch birds for ringing.*

14. In the hand, details of wing length are taken by the ringer to give a guide as to the sex of the bird, males usually being longer winged than females. The bright all blue 'shoulder' to the wing indicates that this bird is over one year old.
15. A Blue Tit in moult: note the growing replacement feathers. The dull greenish smaller feathers on the outer section of the wing contrast with brighter blue elsewhere and indicate that this bird is less than one year old.

17

than may seem necessary, but this may not be the case. Perhaps the essential is to be in the right condition in good time to face the problems that winter poses. If a Blue Tit starts off with suitable reserves, a minimal daily intake will suffice to keep it alive, whereas if it waits until daily food, fat reserves and fatty insulation are all needed at the same time, then its chances of successfully meeting these demands are poor.

As spring advances, the weights of both sexes decline to a low point of around, on average, 10.5 grams (0.37 ounce) in April. Thereafter, the patterns of weight changes for the sexes differ sharply: male weights remain at a low level until the young fledge a month or six weeks later. The female, needing to be in good condition to breed well and anticipating producing an egg daily (a clutch of ten eggs is roughly equivalent to half her body weight) begins a period of brief but dramatic weight increase, partly due to stored fats and partly to the increase in size of her ovaries and associated organs and glands. In a period usually of about three weeks immediately before laying, the average weight of females from a detailed study in Kent rose to almost 13 grams (0.46 ounce) — an increase of about 25 per cent in body weight. In extreme cases, individual female weights occasionally exceeded 14.5 grams (0.51 ounce), a prodigious 40 per cent increase and a clear indication of the need for, and benefits of, courtship feeding.

Though they are slightly shorter in the wing, the weights of young birds are much the same as those of adults of the same sex and parallel their fluctuations.

FLOCKING

Following the fiercely territorial period of early summer, when an area surrounding the nest site is defended with vigour, once the young have been out of the nest for a couple of weeks and have become more mobile, territorial behaviour as such seems to break down. Perhaps this is influenced by the collective stresses of shepherding a large family about and keeping them both safe and well fed. By late summer many of these family groups have merged, often (in large areas of woodland) forming flocks dozens, and sometimes hundreds, of birds strong. These roam noisily and widely, and within them sometimes the family structure will be maintained and a female will be netted close to some of her nestlings for some weeks after they have fledged.

These early days are the most difficult ones for the young Blue Tits. Though the weather is at its most favourable, with long days and high temperatures, and insect food is at its most abundant, the young birds run huge risks of being caught by predators because of their inexperience and, because of their lack of expertise in food gathering, they often perish from starvation or from ailments exacerbated by a poor nutritional status. Ringing studies indicate that summer and early autumn are the peak times for mortality, particularly among young birds, and that those surviving until November have a good chance of reaching the next spring. Using somewhat simplified figures for convenience of demonstration, ringing results allow us to build a picture of how mortality operates in the Blue Tit population.

At the time of fledging, each family consists (say) of two adults and ten juveniles. Detailed population studies indicate that the 'average' pair of Blue Tits at the start of the next breeding season is composed of one experienced adult (having bred at least once before) and one first-year bird, breeding for the first time (one of the previous year's juveniles). Obviously this is an idealised situation — there are also pairs composed of two adults or of two first-year birds. This implies that, between the end of one breeding season and the start of the next, one of each pair of parents dies, to be replaced by one youngster (a 50 per cent adult mortality). But there were ten young, so nine of those have perished, a 90 per cent mortality — high in human eyes but not outstanding in avian population dynamics. Most of this mortality happens well before the winter.

Late in the summer, though the tit flocks in woodland are normally largely composed of Blue and Great Tits, other birds are caught up in the general enthusiasm as the flock sweeps through the trees. Amongst these others are often Chiff-chaffs and Willow Warblers, summer visitors fattening for the journey south, with other woodland birds like Wrens, Goldcrests and Treecreepers. The Goldcrests will often stay with the tits for much of the time, as will the warblers until they depart, but Wrens and Treecreepers seem to join in only as the flock passes through their area of the wood, leaving it after a short while.

Others to join are the remaining members of the tit family, though not all may be present in one woodland. When the variety of tit species is high, then the opportunities are at their best to watch how the available food resources are partitioned, so that competition between related species is minimised. Great Tits, largest of the family and with the stoutest legs and beaks, normally feed on the ground or low on the trunk or major branches, taking food almost like Chaffinches do. If present, Marsh and Willow Tits will feed on the smaller branches in the central part of the tree, while Blue Tits, Coal Tits and Long-tailed Tits will all feed at the extremities of the twigs in the canopy. The apparent conflict between the last three is resolved by marked differences in habitat selection (though often there is ample food, so these are not always involved): the Blue Tit is the deciduous woodland species, and the Long-tailed Tit is a bird of scrub and undergrowth.

Over much of Britain, though Blue Tits may roam the countryside in autumn, they do this over a limited area. Analysis of recoveries of ringed birds shows that

16. *Midwinter inter-site movements at Northward Hill, Kent. The four ringing sites (larger circles) are 200-400 metres (220-440 yards) apart in a large oakwood. Figures within the larger circles indicate the percentage of birds remaining 'faithful' to the area of that ringing site. Figures within the smaller circles indicate the percentage of birds visiting other sites as indicated by the arrows. Clearly there is considerable site fidelity, even within a habitat that seems ecologically relatively uniform to human eyes.*

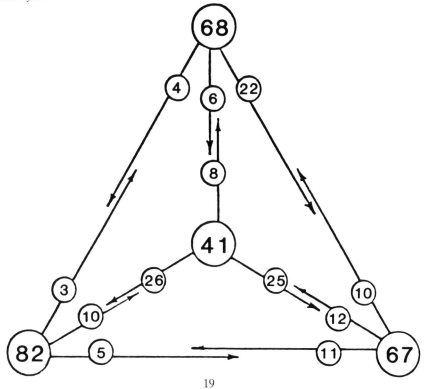

17. *Amongst many learned habits, opening milk bottles to reach the nutritious cream typifies the Blue Tit's opportunistic approach to feeding.*

relatively few (about 14 per cent) of Blue Tits move more than 10 km (6 miles) from the place of ringing, and fewer than one per cent are recovered at distances in excess of 100 km (60 miles). Movements are most frequent, and distances greatest, among birds in northern England and Scotland and amongst those venturing into upland woods to breed in summer. Here it is the severity of winter that forces birds south or to seek warmer areas.

Over much of northern continental Europe, however, migration is a routine, and over long distances. In some years the numbers of birds moving is so great that migrating continental tits (recognisable by their plumage in some cases, as well as by their rings) reach Britain. Such events are known as 'irruptions', and

these seem to follow a series of good breeding seasons and mild winters with an adequate food supply. These allow Blue Tit numbers to build up to such an extent that eventually the sheer weight of numbers imposes an impossible strain on the available food, and possibly also on the tits' social organisation.

Every so often — perhaps on average once in a decade or two — huge numbers of continental Blue Tits descend on eastern England. The last times this occurred were in 1957 and in 1974, when, late in the autumn, coastal towns and fields in eastern England were full of Blue Tits, the reed beds in some marshland ditches holding hundreds of birds at times. Not only were the numbers extraordinary, so too was their behaviour. No milk bottle was safe and there were many complaints about Blue Tits entering houses and tearing off strips of wallpaper.

As the days begin to shorten appreciably towards the end of the year, natural mortality will have already reduced flock sizes, and the large flocks break up into smaller, often much less mobile groups. In a long-term study in deciduous (mostly oak) woodland in Kent, it seemed that the Blue Tits spread themselves fairly uniformly over the whole wood at the onset of winter, and most then moved only within a fairly closely defined area, perhaps only 300-400 metres (330-440 yards) across, whatever the temptations might have been in neighbouring areas. This group wintering area was not as actively defended as is a breeding territory, but the boundaries seemed to be reasonably sacrosanct, right through the winter. In subsequent winters birds surviving from previous years sometimes chose a different area or sometimes remained as before. The only event that moved almost all the tits out — often to the adjacent village — was a period of several days' snowfall. After the thaw they returned to their previous locations.

Though urban and suburban areas are often a degree or two warmer than the surrounding country, have numerous roosting sites and, because of the abundant food put out for Blue Tits on bird tables by enthusiastic householders, would seem to be a luxurious habitat, this is evidently not the case, and town tits seem to spend the winter roaming much more widely in search of food than their rural cousins.

Most tits roost in sheltered crevices or holes, which must help reduce the energy they expend in keeping warm over long winter nights. They normally roost alone, even driving off others which try to join them. The female often may roost in the hole in which she ultimately nests. Some Blue Tits choose even warmer nesting sites: in parts of London and in Salisbury Blue Tits are known to roost in street lamps. The birds find a way in between the lamp and the shade and roost (albeit in rather bright conditions) with the benefit of shelter from the wind and considerable heat from the bulb.

Blue Tits and man

NESTBOXES

Much of our detailed knowledge of Blue Tits and the lives they lead stems from their habit of regularly accepting man-made nestboxes as suitable nest sites. Such boxes can have glass observation panels or, better, a latched lifting lid (or removable front panel) that allows easy inspection of the nestbox contents. Detailed scientific work is carried out by university and amateur researchers, often using 'colonies' of dozens or even hundreds of nestboxes in suitable woodland, but an enormous number of people, ranging from birdwatching enthusiasts to ordinary householders, simply enjoy the pleasures of watching a Blue Tit family going about its daily life in a nestbox in the garden. In some parts of Britain and Ireland, and in many other countries, large numbers of nestboxes are installed by foresters to encourage the build-up of a high tit population in forests, well managed timber having relatively few natural nest sites, in the hope that the birds will prevent harmful foliage-eating caterpillars from reaching pest status.

The Blue Tit seems relatively unaffected by nestbox design, or by indifferent carpentry. The box should be safe from collapse; it should be firmly fixed to the tree or building (but on trees destined to be sawn for timber the fixing should be a strap, copper nails or hardwood peg); it should have adequate drainage at floor level; it should be positioned away from interference (usually human); and it should be set so that it is protected from strong prevailing winds, driving rain and hot sunshine.

An effective and versatile box would follow roughly the dimensions in figure 18, fashioned from a plank 4 feet by 6 inches by ¾ inch. If metric timber is used then the plans can be redrawn on the basis that one inch approximates to 2.5 cm, one foot to 30 cm. Following the cutting diagram, construction is reasonably simple, joints being held either with screws or with 2 inch (50 mm) oval nails.

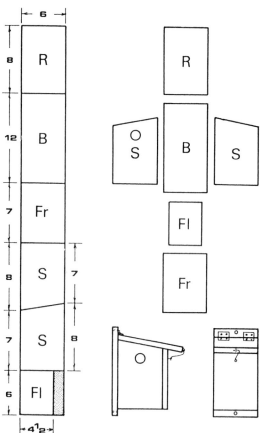

18. *A simple but practical design of nestbox suitable for Blue Tits. Dimensions are given in inches. A cheap and readily available source of timber is second-hand floor boards, which are normally 6 inches (152 mm) wide.*

Second-hand timber is perfectly acceptable, as is softwood, while the 'rustic' appearance conveyed by offcuts with bark attached, though aesthetically pleasing, often entails constructional complexity. If a timber preservative is used, it should be applied several weeks before the breeding season.

The entrance hole is normally positioned in one side to allow a little extra depth, but a front entrance can be used and the catch moved to the side of the box. In either case the lid should be positioned to give a sheltering overhang. The lid may be hinged with a rustless metal or plastic hinge (or a flexible strip of plastic or leather) or simply held under a metal or wooden flange. Blue Tits (and several other birds) will enter holes between 1 inch and 1⅛ inches (25 to 28 mm) diameter but a larger entrance-hole will admit House and Tree Sparrows.

The box can be positioned anywhere between 4 and 16 feet (1.2 and 5 metres) off the ground, depending on the risks of disturbance and on convenience. Acceptable nestbox densities vary, but in most circumstances adjacent boxes should be at least 30 feet (9 metres) apart, otherwise the females may be confused and lay in each other's nests. A perching twig outside the hole may seem useful but is more likely to help predators like squirrels or Weasels. In suburban surrounds, nestboxes should be well away from places where cats could lurk or pounce. Boxes are best erected during the winter, the earlier the better, and at the latest by early March.

Through the rest of the year, Blue Tits will come readily to garden bird feeding stations of all descriptions, feeding on most items put out for them: the range of food taken is far too long for description.

22

Less acceptable habits are paper tearing, usually associated with migrant flocks (see above) and quite unusual, and the opening of milk bottles to drink the cream, which is now widespread and commonplace. This habit was first recorded in the Southampton area in 1929. In the next few years it spread rapidly over Britain and was also reported from much of Europe The change from the easily pecked-open cardboard caps to aluminium foil caused no problems, nor did the change from tall bottles to squat ones. The waxed carton seemed impregnable for many years, but now even these fall victim, and they cannot be protected in the traditional way with an inverted plastic cup.

BLUE TITS AND FRUIT CROPS

Fruit farmers and gardeners have long complained about winter bud damage caused by Blue Tits, almost always mistakenly as the tits are seeking only insect eggs and larvae. Bud damage is caused by the Bullfinch and, to a lesser extent, the House Sparrow. However, a potentially more serious problem has been recognised: ripening fruit damage. Ripening fruit, often colourful and soft, is prone to attack by a number of birds and insects, eager to reach its moist, sugar-rich flesh. Studies have shown that much of this damage is initiated by Blue Tits, often long before the fruit is ripe. Tiny exploratory pecks made on the shoulders of apples or pears penetrate the tough skin. Then, or later, Blue Tits, Song Thrushes, Blackbirds, Starlings and even Greenfinches will enlarge the original wound and effectively ruin the fruit. Detailed investigation has revealed that wasps, too, normally follow up Blue Tit pecks, rather than chewing into the fruit themselves as had long been thought to be the case. Smaller organisms, like fungal spores, may also invade the wound, and the consequent rot often spreads to damage adjacent fruit in the cluster. In many orchards and gardens each year, Blue Tits are responsible in this way for the loss of 5 or 10 per cent of the usable fruit, but in some areas and in some years damage to commercial orchards may

19. A Blue Tit extracts a Codling Moth larva from its overwintering site, concealed deep within a crevice in the bark of an apple-tree trunk.

exceed 20 per cent of the marketable crop, an unacceptable level. Unfortunately there is no remedy: the multitude of scaring devices and repellent chemical sprays on the market have no lasting effect on damage levels.

But not all Blue Tit activity in orchards is to the farmers' detriment. One of the major apple and pear orchard insect pests, and one of the most difficult to control, even with the more lethal of available insecticides, is the Codling Moth. The moth itself is inconspicuous, small and drably brown, but its larva is much better known as the fat, pinkish white maggot, with a brown head, sometimes revealed as you bite deep into the heart of a juicy apple. One reason that chemical control is so difficult against Codling is that the time between the hatching of the tiny caterpillar and its reaching safety by burrowing deep into the apple is very brief — often only hours or a day or two at most. Thus it is at other stages in the life cycle of the pest that control measures must be directed. The overwintering larva, tucked away in a silken cocoon behind a flake of bark on the trunk, would seem to be as safe as the larva in the apple, and chemical sprays cannot reach it there, but it is vulnerable to biological control as exercised by Blue Tits.

Researchers working in cider apple orchards in south-west England found that almost all the Codling larvae were removed from their hidden cocoons during the winter. In two successive years of experiments, about 95 per cent of the larvae were eventually found and eaten, many of them in the first couple of weeks after they had emerged from the apple, crawled into their crevice and spun a protective cocoon. The researchers suggested that even if this continued high level of predation did not in itself provide effective biological control, preventing, in unsprayed orchards, an 'explosion' of the Codling Moth population, it opened the way for other limiting factors (other predators, frosts, disease and so on) to achieve this.

The Blue Tit remains one of a select few birds destined, it seems, always to be in close proximity to man. In some circumstances, like predation on milk bottles or fruit, the close association may be troublesome, but far more often, for the opportunities it offers for study (ranging from casual to detailed) or simply for enjoyment, the Blue Tit remains, rightly, amongst the most popular of birds.

Further reading

Flegg, J. J. M., and Cox, C. J. 'The Moult of British Great and Blue Tits', *Bird Study* *16*, 147-57 (1969).

Flegg, J. J. M., and Glue, D. E. *Nestboxes*. Field Guide 3, British Trust for Ornithology, Tring, 1971.

Lack, D. *Population Studies of Birds*. Clarendon Press, Oxford, 1966.

Perrins, C. M. *British Tits*. Collins (New Naturalist Series 62), 1979. (This is the key volume for all interested in tits of any species. Extremely comprehensive yet readable, a mine of information and further reference sources.)

Solomon, M. E., and Glen, D. M. 'Prey Density and Rates of Predation by Tits *(Parus* spp.) on Larvae of Codling Moth *(Cydia pomonella)* under Bark', *Journal of Applied Ecology, 16*, 49-59 (1979).

ACKNOWLEDGEMENTS

The following photographs are reproduced by courtesy of the Frank Lane Picture Agency and are acknowledged to: John Hawkins, cover; Eric and David Hosking, 4, 6, 7, 8, 9; Roger Hosking, 1; Ronald Thompson, 17; Graham I. Wren, 5. Photograph 19 is reproduced by courtesy of M. E. Solomon and the editors of the Journal of Applied Ecology. Figures 10 and 16 are reproduced from J. J. M. Flegg's *Birdwatchers' Year,* by courtesy of T. and A. D. Poyser Ltd. All other illustrations are by the author.